Right@Sight

a progressive sight-reading course
including duet parts and a CD of accompaniments

Violin Grade 1

Caroline Lumsden

with accompaniments
by Anita Hewitt-Jones

Time
Rhythm
and
Key

LONDON · FRANKFURT/M · LEIPZIG · NEW YORK
www.editionpeters.com

Preface

Sight-reading is one of the most important yet neglected aspects of learning an instrument. If treated as an integral and enjoyable part of teaching from an early stage, it is easy to achieve considerable success. The *Right@Sight* series for violin and cello, developed by Caroline Lumsden and Anita Hewitt-Jones, is a very thorough approach that, if followed systematically, will produce excellent sight-readers and will more than prepare students for their graded examinations.

Right@Sight Violin Grade 1 is divided into 3 sections: preliminary (pre-grade 1); section 1 (grade 1 – easier) and section 2 (grade 1 – harder). These sections are designed to help students progress smoothly from one grade to the next. A student completing both sections 1 and 2 before taking a grade 1 examination will be supremely confident at sight-reading.

Throughout this book, each double-page spread has a page of solo examples with helpful hints, followed by a page of duets to play with a teacher or friend. Students are encouraged always to use the mnemonic **TraK** before sight-reading any piece:

> **T**ime signature: always check the time signature of a piece
> **R**hythm: clap the rhythm while saying the time names or singing the note names
> **a**nd
> **K**ey: always check the key signature of a piece and check what finger pattern is needed for that key

There are also *On your own* sections, containing pieces similar to those presented in the exam room – i.e. without any tips or audio accompaniments.

Encourage pupils to sing with note names e.g. D E Fs (pronounced "efs") All sharps have an "s" sound after the note and all flats an "f" sound (e.g. Bf is pronounced "beef"). Good intonation then becomes second nature.

To encourage rhythmic playing, particularly with young children, saying the rhythm in words can help to achieve real success:

Time names	Symbols	Time names	Symbols
slow	♩	quick-er	♩. ♩
ssh!	𝄽	quick-e-ty	3 ♪♪♪
quick quick	♪♪	sh!	𝄾
semiquaver	♬♬	snap-py	♪ ♩.
quick-semi	♪♬		
semi-quick	♬♪	compound time names	
slow-ow	𝅗𝅥	slow	♩.
slow-ow-ow	𝅗𝅥.	slow-ow	𝅗𝅥.
slow-ow-ow-ow	𝅝	quickety	♪♪♪
slow-er and	♩. ♪	qui-cker and	♩.♪♪

© Copyright 2006 by Hinrichsen Edition, Peters Edition Ltd, London
Cover design by Adam Hay
Music setting by Robin Hagues
Printed in England by Halstan & Co., Amersham, Bucks.

Contents

The CD

A CD accompaniment to the solos has been provided to enable pupils to practise sight-reading between lessons, when there is no teacher to help. In order to encourage the student to play rhythmically and in time, the accompaniments in the preliminary section of the book (piece numbers 1–32) double the rhythm of the violin part. From the beginning of section 1 (starting with piece 33), the violinist needs to hold their own rhythm, although the accompaniments are still designed to help the student play in time.

We suggest that the violinist first plays the piece without the CD accompaniment. Each accompaniment on the CD is played twice, separated by metronome clicks which keep the pulse going through both playings. The violinist can use these accompaniments in a number of ways. The first playing can be used to clap the rhythm, with or without the time or note names (see preface). The metronome clicks between the two playings are intended to give the student time to get ready to play, so it is possible to clap on the first time through and play on the second. Or the student could clap through twice, then replay the track and play through twice. In 2/4 and 3/4 time signatures there are two bars of metronome clicks; in 4/4 there is one bar of clicks.

Acknowledgements

Alan Lumsden and Kate Allott for hours spent at the computer,
offering advice and playing duets

Time
Rhythm
and
Key

Open strings:
crotchets and quavers in 2/4 and 4/4

Solos

Follow the **TRaK**

Play these solos without the CD backing first.

Always check the time signature **T** and rhythm **R** before starting to play.

1

T Look at the music below. What does the time signature tell you?

R Clap and say the rhythm (slow slow slow slow quick quick quick quick slow slow . . .) before playing. Which bars have quavers?

When playing, make a good firm sound.

? Where is there a crotchet rest?

Confidently

CLAP/SAY: slow slow slow slow quick quick quick quick slow slow quick quick quick quick slow slow slow slow slow ssh!

2

T Look at the time signature. The top figure has changed. How many beats are there in a bar now?

R Clap and say the rhythm. Which bars have the same rhythm?

Play as smoothly as possible with a good tone.

! Cross the strings carefully in bars 2 and 3.

Smoothly

CLAP/SAY: slow slow quick quick quick quick quick quick quick quick slow slow slow slow quick quick quick quick slow slow slow ssh!

3

T What is the time signature?

R Clap and say the rhythm before playing. When clapping, say 'ssh!' for the rests and indicate them with an outward movement of the hands.

Play with a strong sound, keeping in time.

! Watch out for the rests. Make a circular movement with the bow arm, ready for the next down-bow.

Boldly

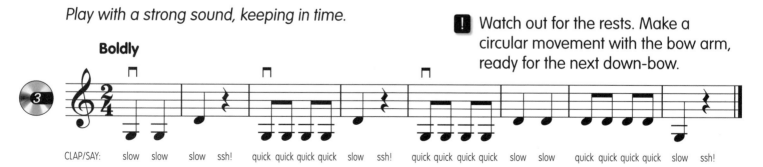

CLAP/SAY: slow slow slow ssh! quick quick quick quick slow ssh! quick quick quick quick slow slow quick quick quick quick slow ssh!

Duets

Duets are great fun to play. Your part is the top line.

4 *Check the time signature, then look ahead for the bars with quavers or rests before playing straight through with your teacher.*

Firmly

5

Lively

6

Rhythmically

5

Solos

Follow the **TRaK**

Play these solos without the CD backing first.

7 **T** Look at the time signature. There are now three beats in a bar.

R Clap the rhythm emphasising the first beat. Don't forget the time names:
quick quick slow slow . . .

Play through with a light bouncy feel. A waltz is a dance in 3/4 time with a slight emphasis on the first beat of the bar.

? Look at bars 1–4 and 5–8. Are the notes or rhythm the same?

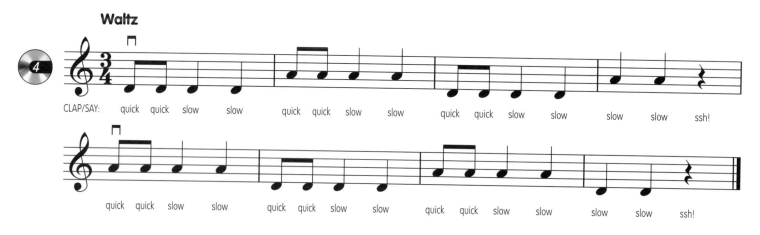

8 **T** How many crotchet beats are there in a bar?

R Can you tap the rhythm? Notice which bars have rests, and on which beat of the bar the quavers appear.

Keep the quavers rhythmical and play confidently.

! Hold the minims for two full beats but don't play through the rests.

Duets

Play the top line of these duets with another violinist or with your teacher.

9

With a lilt

10 *Watch out for the up-bow string crossings in bars 3, 4 and 7.*

Calmly

Solos

Play these solos without the CD backing first.

11 **T** How many crotchet beats are there in a bar? How many semiquavers in a crotchet?

R Clap and say the time names (se–mi–qua–ver quick quick . . .) before playing.

Play through steadily using shorter bows for the semiquavers.

? How many bars have semiquavers in them?

CLAP/SAY: se - mi - qua-ver quick quick slow   slow   se - mi - qua-ver quick quick se - mi-qua-ver quick quick se - mi - qua - ver quick quick slo - ow

12 **T** How many crotchet beats are there in a bar? Look at the top figure of the time signature.

R Clap carefully. Note that bars 1 and 3 have the same rhythm. How many times does the rhythm ♫♫♫ appear?

Don't start too fast. Bow freely and play with a good sound.

! Remember to make a circular movement with your bowing arm during the rest.

CLAP/SAY: quick quick quick quick se-mi-qua-ver quick quick quick quick quick quick slow ssh! . . .

13 **T** What is the time signature?

R Which bars have semiquavers and on which beat of the bar do they appear? Clap the rhythm carefully while saying the time names.

Slightly emphasise the first beat of each bar to help keep time.

! Watch out for the semiquavers on the second beat of the bar.

CLAP/SAY: quick quick quick quick quick quick   se - mi - qua-ver quick quick quick quick . . .

Duets

Play the top line of these duets with another violinist or with your teacher.

14

Slowly and rhythmically

15

Cheerfully

Solos

Follow the **TRaK**

Play these solos without the CD backing first.

16

T How many quavers are there in one bar of 2/4 time? Look at bar 2 to help you.

R Clap the rhythm before you play. Can you spot two identical bars?

! Sing through with note names (D E DDAA B B A A . . .) before playing.

Make a good sound as you play through, without stopping.

! Which bars have first-finger notes? Have the first finger ready to play before you begin the piece.

Gently

17

T What does the time signature tell you? Remember to look at the top figure.

R This is a longer piece so clap carefully saying time names.

? On which beats of the bar do the first-finger notes appear?

Play this through using plenty of bow on the crotchets and minims.

! Keep the first finger ready, especially for the A on the bottom string.

Freely

CLAP/SAY: slow   slow   quick quick quick quick   slow   slow   slow   slow . . .

Duets

Play the top line of these duets with another violinist or with your teacher.

18

Happily

19

Lively

Solos

Follow the **TRaK**

Play these solos without the CD backing first.

20

T What is the time signature?

R Clap and then say the note names in rhythm: G A G G . . .

? Which bars start with a first finger?

Emphasise the first beat of each bar to give this a 'waltz' feel.

! Watch out for the crotchet rests in bars 4 and 8.

21

T What does the time signature tell you?

R Clap and say the rhythm with note names: E F♯ (pronounce this "efs") E F♯ . . .

? There are two different rhythm patterns. What are they?

Clap bars 2 and 3 before you start.

! Before you play with the bow, tap the fingering of bars 1, 5 and 6 on the fingerboard.

Duets

Play the top line of these duets with another violinist or with your teacher.

22

23

Solos

Play these solos without the CD backing first.

Always check the time signature **T** rhythm **R** and key **K** before starting to play.

24

T How many crotchet beats are there in a bar?

R Look ahead to see where the quavers appear.

K The key signature of F♯ tells you that the piece is in G major.

Play steadily at a slow walking pace.

? Which bars have second-finger B in them?

25

T What is the time signature?

R Clap and sing or say the note names: D D E E F♯ ("efs") . . .

K The key signature of two sharps tells you that this piece is in D major. Look at the first and last notes of the piece. What do you notice?

Keep the quavers light and look ahead to prepare the fingers.

! Find all the second-finger F♯s.

26

T What does the time signature tell you?

R Clap and say the note names: A B C♯ ("sees") . . .

K The key signature of three sharps tells you that the key is A major.

? Compare bars 1–4 and 5–8. Are the notes the same? Is the rhythm the same?

Play this smoothly and expressively.

? Which bars have a second-finger C♯? Which have G♯?

Duets

From here on you will notice that the parts do not always have the same rhythms as each other.
Spot the differences before you play!

27

Gently

28

March-like

Solos

Follow the **TRaK**

Play these solos without the CD backing first.

29

T How many beats are there in each bar?

R Clap carefully and sing the note names.

K What do two sharps in the key signature tell you?

! Compare bars 5 and 6 with bars 1 and 2. What is the difference?

Play with a dance-like feel. Remember to keep your high second and third fingers close together.

! Look out for the new third-finger note (G).

30

T What is the time signature?

R Say the note names in rhythm.

K Name the key note.

! Point to all the C♯s and G♯s which are followed by third fingers a semitone higher.

Look ahead and play boldly.

! Be ready for the string crossing in the last bar and make sure that the top A is in tune with the lower A.

Duets

Play the top line of these duets with another violinist or with your teacher.

31

Steadily

32 *Watch out for the rests in your part.*

Brightly

Moving by step in G, D and A majors

Solos

Play these solos without the CD backing first.

33

T What is the time signature? Note that quavers can be grouped in fours in this time signature.

R Say the note names aloud as you clap. Is the last note the same as the first?

K What key is this piece in? Which bar has a semitone F♯ to G?

? How long do you hold the last note?

Play with a good firm sound.

! These pieces all use the 0 – 1 – high 2 – 3 finger pattern.

34

T What is the time signature?

R Say the note names.

K What is the key? Name the sharps. To help you remember key signatures, think of your open strings – G major has one sharp, D major has two sharps, A major has three sharps. How many sharps does E major have?

Play through in a quick and lively manner.

! Have your third finger ready for bar 5.

Duets

Play the top line of these duets with another violinist or with your teacher.

35

Briskly

36

Happily

Solos

Play these solos without the CD backing first.

37

T Is this piece in duple or triple (2 or 3) time?

R Clap the rhythm with time names before you play. Look to see which beats of the bar have semiquavers.

K What is the key? Does the piece end on the keynote?

Keep moving along freely and rhythmically.

! Watch the string crossings. Be ready with your fourth finger in bar four.

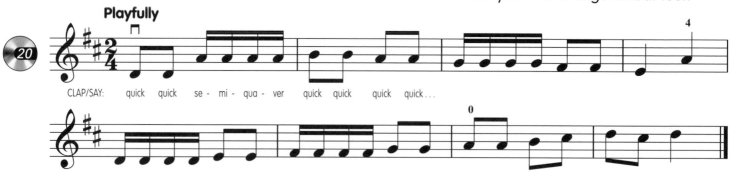

CLAP/SAY: quick   quick   se - mi - qua - ver   quick   quick   quick   quick . . .

38

T What is the time signature?

R How many bars in this piece have the same rhythm?

K Name the key and the first note.

Keep this light and energetic, using short bow-strokes.

! Watch out for the fourth finger in bar 4 and the string crossing in bar 7.

Duets

Play the top line of these duets with another violinist or with your teacher.

39 *Listen carefully to the second violin part. It will help you keep the semiquavers in time.*

Carefully

40

Cheekily

Solos

Follow the **TRaK**

Play these solos without the CD backing first.

41

T How many crotchet beats are there in a semibreve?

R How long do you hold the last note for? Keep the bow moving at a slow, even speed.

K Name the sharps in the key signature.

Play this at a steady walking pace and remember to give the last note its full value.

! Have your third finger ready to play in bar 6.

42

T How many crotchet beats do you count on a dotted minim?

R Clap carefully, singing the note names.

K Which note do you start on and which finger do you play it with? What note do you end on?

Play this through using the whole bow for the dotted minims.

43

T How many quavers are there in a minim? Look at bar 5 for a clue.

R Clap carefully. How long is the rest in bar 4?

K What note do you start on? Check it against your open G string to make sure it is in tune.

Look ahead as you play. Don't be caught out by the rests.

! Be careful in the last bar. Remember to hold the semibreve for a full four beats – use a slow bow.

Duets

Play the top line of these duets with another violinist or with your teacher.

44 *Remember to hold all the long notes for their full value. Listen to the accompanying crotchets to help keep time.*

Bright walking pace

45

With movement

23

Solos

Play these solos without the CD backing first.

46

T What is the time signature?

R Say the rhythm through with time names: quick se–mi quick quick . . .

K What is the key? Name the sharps. Find the semitone C♯ to D.

! Beware of bars 5 and 6. How does the rhythm differ from bars 1 and 2?

Don't start the piece too quickly. Keep the rhythm as crisp as you can.

! Have your third finger ready at the start of bar 6.

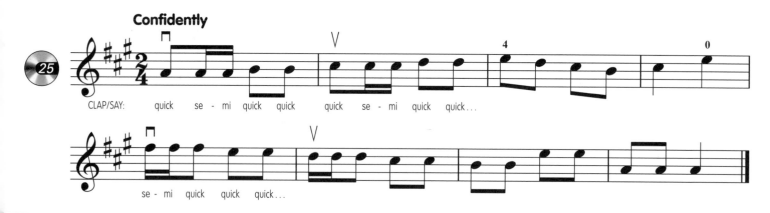

47

T What is the time signature?

R Work out the patterns of quavers and semiquavers by clapping and saying the rhythms. Hold the last minim for its full value.

K Before you begin, play the key note. What note do you start on?

Look at the bowing in bars 5 and 6 and then play through rhythmically.

! Watch out for bar 3.

Duets

Play the top line of these duets with another violinist or with your teacher.

48 *Clap through with time names before playing.*

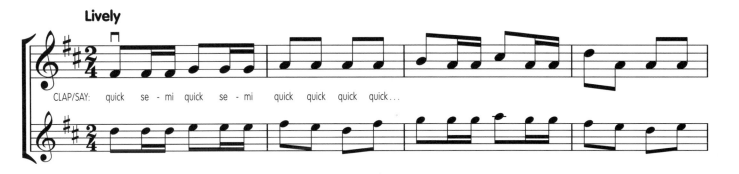

CLAP/SAY: quick se - mi quick se - mi quick quick quick quick . . .

49

Solos

Follow the **TRaK**

Play these solos without the CD backing first.

50

T What is the time signature?

R Keep the slurred pairs of crotchets exactly in time.

K What note does the melody end on?

Check which bars have slurs in them before playing through gently.

? Which bars have semitones?

51

T Is this duple, triple or quadruple (2, 3 or 4) time?

R Clap the rhythm. Note which notes are slurred.

K Name the sharps in the key signature.

? Where is there a C♯ after an open E string? Have your second finger ready to play in plenty of time.

Play as smoothly as possible with a sweet tone.

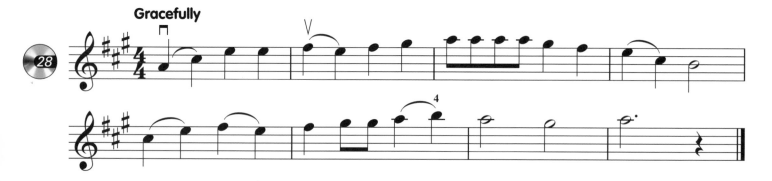

Duets

Play the top line of these duets with another violinist or with your teacher.

Walking speed

53 *Your three crotchets in a bow in the first bar set the speed of this piece.*
Check the fingering before you play.

Flowing

Solos

Follow the **TRaK**

Play these solos without the CD backing first.

54

T What is the time signature?

R Count steadily. Don't hurry.

K The melody uses an arpeggio of which key? Name the notes of the arpeggio.

Play crisply, keeping the bow-stroke short and neat.

! Watch out for the slurred quavers in bar 6.

55

T Is this duple, triple or quadruple (2, 3 or 4) time?

R Look carefully at bars 2 and 4 before clapping through.

K In which bars does an A major arpeggio appear?

Play with a bright, lively tone and make sure you hold the dotted minim for its full value.

! Have your second finger ready in bar 1 as you play the downward arpeggio.

Duets

Play the top line of these duets with another violinist or with your teacher.

56

With energy

57

Playfully

Solos

Follow the **TRaK**

Play these solos without the CD backing first.

58

T What is the time signature?

R Give the crotchet after the quavers its full value.

K What is the key? Name the highest note.

! Watch for which quavers are slurred and which are separate.

Play through gracefully, observing the dynamics.

! What do *p*, *f* and *grazioso* mean? Make sure you know the meanings of Italian musical words.

59

T What is the time signature?

R What do you notice about bars 1–4 and 9–12?

K Does this piece start on the keynote? Name the first note.

? What do ⦏ and ⦐ mean?

Be prepared for the interval of a sixth from F♯ to A before playing through.

! Get louder (*crescendo*) and quieter (*diminuendo*) as marked.

Duets

Play the top line of these duets with another violinist or with your teacher.

60 *What do mf and alla marcia mean?*

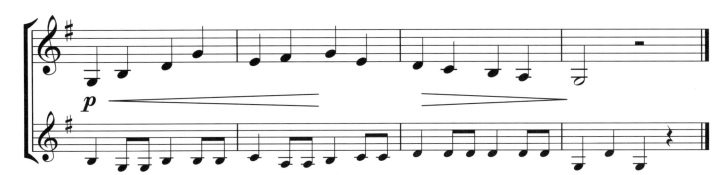

61 *What do vivace and rit mean?*

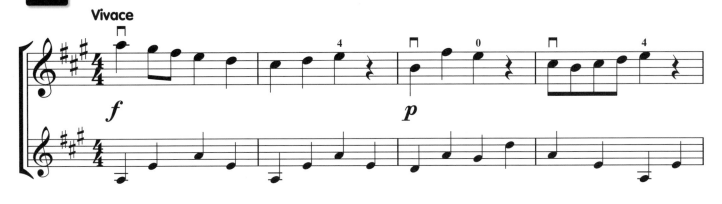

Solos

Follow the **TRaK**

Play the following pieces on your own. The tempo or mood indications in English or Italian will tell you the character of the piece. Always remember to check the TRaK.

T Look at the time signature. When you have decided how fast to play, keep a steady beat.

R Clap the rhythm, then try any tricky bits on their own. Count carefully and don't try to play too fast.

K The key signature tells you which sharps and flats to play. Think of the fingering you will use.

After giving yourself a minute or two to look at all these things, including the expression marks, play through the piece without stopping. Don't panic! Keep going, whatever happens, and play confidently.

Solos

Play these solos without the CD backing first.

70

T Is this piece in duple or triple time?

R Count carefully, and hold the last note for its full value.

K This piece uses two octaves of which major scale? Which bars have the second finger close to the first finger?

Play through gently, remembering to hold the dotted minim for its full value.

! Look ahead to prepare the string crossings and slurs.

71

T What is the time signature?

R Pretend to bow while humming in time. Notice where the slurs appear.

K What note does this piece start and end on? Can you find a scale in this piece?

Play with a good lively sound, getting stronger towards the end.

! Name the second-finger note in bar 6. Is it played with a high or low second finger?

72

T How many crotchet beats are there in a bar in this new time signature?

R Count carefully, especially the dotted minims. Emphasise the first beat of the bar.

K What is the key? Where do the semitones appear?

Keep the beat rhythmic throughout and observe the expression marks.

! Note that the beats are mostly grouped in either 2+3 or 3+2. Where do the accents appear?

Duets

Play the top line of these duets with another violinist or with your teacher.

73 *Count the long notes carefully in 5/4 time. What does* con moto *mean?*

74 *What does* allegro ritmico *mean?*

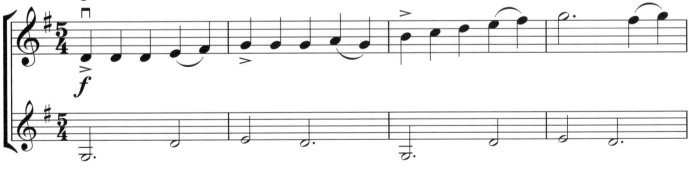

Solos

Follow the **TRaK**

Play these solos without the CD backing first.

75

T What is the time signature?

R Remember to indicate the rests when you clap.

K What note do you start and finish on?

? In bars 3, 5 and 6, is the second finger high or low? Play the scale of C major to get used to the finger pattern.

Keep the music moving, but don't be caught out by the rests.

? What does *con moto* mean?

76

T What is the time signature?

R Clap and say the note names before playing.

K Play the key note before you start.

? What does *dolce* mean?

Play smoothly, making a contrast between the mf and mp sections.

? How much bow should you use for the minim slurred to a crotchet in bars 2, 4 and 6?

Duets

Play the top line of these duets with another violinist or with your teacher.

77

78 *What do you think* energico *means?*

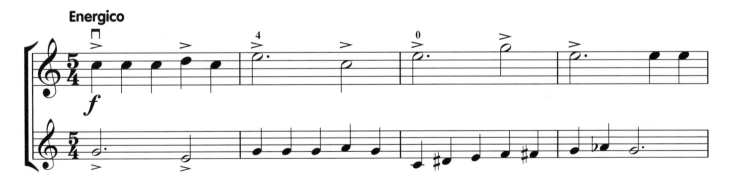

Solos

Play these solos without the CD backing first.

79

T What is the time signature?

R Clap and say the rhythm with time names. Tap the beat with your foot while clapping the off-beat rhythm in bar 2. Lighten the quavers and emphasise the crotchets.

K Does this piece start on the keynote? Spot the semitones.

Play through in a lively fashion.

! Watch out for the quaver rests.

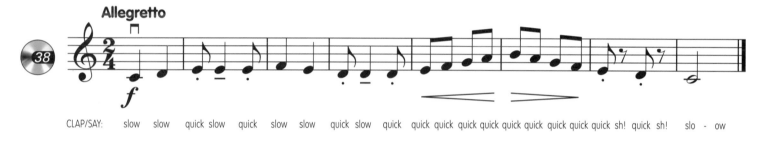

CLAP/SAY: slow slow quick slow quick slow slow quick slow quick quick quick quick quick quick quick quick quick quick sh! quick sh! slo - ow

80

T What is the time signature?

R Clap the rhythm with time names. Take care with bar 7.

K What note do you start on? Check third-finger D with the open D string.

? In which bar should you use a low second finger?

Give a lively performance, emphasising the first quaver of the off-beat rhythm. Watch out for the sudden p in bar 3.

! A tango is a South-American dance that uses the rhythm ♪♩ ♪♩ ♩

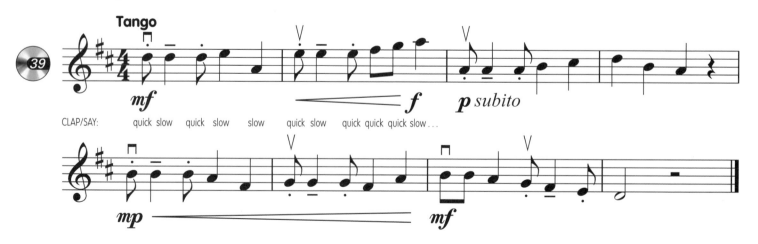

CLAP/SAY: quick slow quick slow slow quick slow quick quick quick slow . . .

Duets

Play the top line of these duets with another violinist or with your teacher.

81 *Clap before you play. Use time names to help you. It is great fun playing off-beat rhythms against a steady beat. What does scherzando mean?*

Scherzando

82 *Watch for the "snap-py" rhythm in bar 7.*

Allegro

CLAP/SAY: quick   slow   quick   snap - py   slo - ow

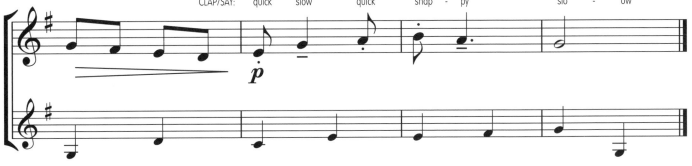

Solos

Follow the **TRaK**

Play these solos without the CD backing first.

83

T Is this piece in duple or quadruple time?

R Clap the dotted rhythm of bars 1 and 2 before playing.

K What is the key? Which finger pattern should you use?

? How many bars have a dotted rhythm?

Use a faster bow for the single quaver, but always play with a beautiful sound, as if you are singing.

? What does *cantabile* mean?

CLAP/SAY: slow - er and slow   slow   slow - er and slow   slow...

84

T Name a type of dance in 3/4 time.

R Clap the dotted rhythm carefully.

K Does this piece begin on the key note? Spot the semitones.

Keep this moving calmly and smoothly, observing all the dynamics.

? What does *dolce* mean?

Duets

Play the top line of these duets with another violinist or with your teacher.

85

86

Solos

Play these solos without the CD backing first.

87

T 3/8 = three quaver beats in a bar. How many beats do you count on the first note of bar 3?

R Clap the 3/8 rhythm and count in quavers.

K The key signature looks like C major, but is in fact A minor.

! Watch out for the repeat sign and be ready to retake the bow. On the second time through, leave out the first-time bar and jump straight to the second.

Play through slowly with a beautiful sound.

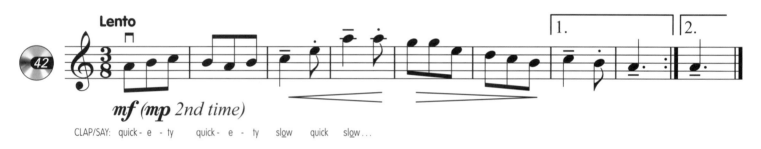

mf (mp 2nd time)

CLAP/SAY: quick - e - ty   quick - e - ty   slow   quick   slow . . .

88

T What is the time signature?

R Clap carefully. Which bars have a quaver rest?

K What is the key? Do you start on the key note?

! Be ready for the octave jump and retake in the final two bars.

Keep the quavers moving at a moderate speed.

! Remember to repeat from the beginning and jump to the second-time bar.

mp (mf 2nd time)

Duets

Play the top line of these duets with another violinist or with your teacher.

Tranquillo

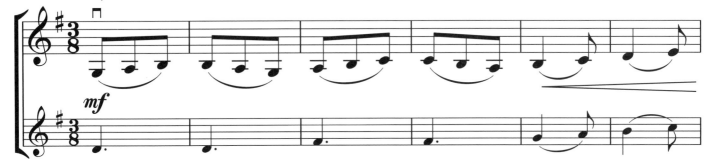

 What does giocoso *mean?*

Giocoso

Solos

Play these solos without the CD backing first.

91

T 6/8 has six quavers in a bar, grouped together in threes.

R Clap and say the rhythm – feel it as two dotted crotchets in a bar. In bars 1, 2, 5 and 7, emphasise the first and fourth quavers.

K What is the key? Where do the semitones appear?

Play through in a lively manner.

? What does *con brio* mean?

CLAP/SAY: quick-e-ty quick-e-ty quick-e-ty quick-e-ty slow quick slow quick slow . . .

92

T How many quavers are there in a bar?

R Emphasise the first and fourth quavers when you clap and play. The slurred quavers help give a feel of two dotted crotchets in a bar.

K Name the key.

? Which bar has a *crescendo*, and which a *diminuendo*?

Use long smooth bows and let the music sing.

! Have your third finger ready in bar 3, and watch out for the slurred octave jump.

Duets

Play the top line of these duets with another violinist or with your teacher.

93 *What does* andante *mean?*
Spot an ascending and a descending arpeggio.

Andante

94 *What does* leggiero *mean?*

Leggiero

Solos

Although there are no hints to help you through the following pieces, keep checking the TRaK.

99

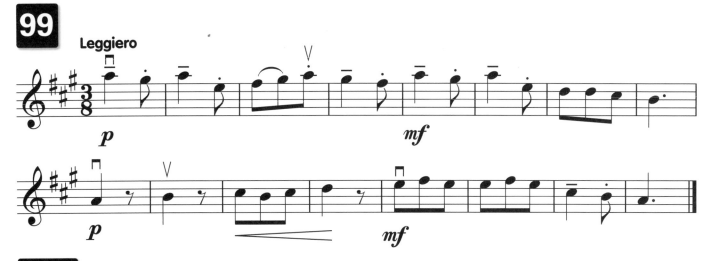

100

101

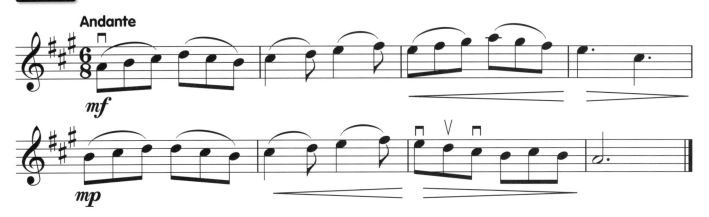

102

103

Giocoso

104

Andante

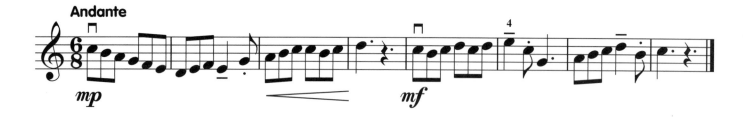

105

Allegro

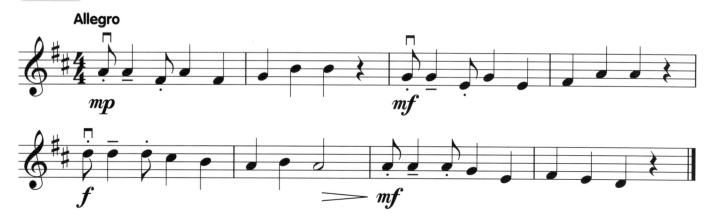

106

Energico